Contents

This Agreement is made the _____ 20 _____

Between (1)

_____

_____

_____ (Company No._____)[1]

of/whose registered office is at _____

_____

_____ ('the Sub-Contractor')

And (2) MIDAS CONSTRUCTION LIMITED

_____

_____ (Company No. 1240442)[1]

of/whose registered office is at PYNES HILL, EXETER,

EX2 SWS

_____ ('the Main Contractor')

[1] Where the Sub-Contractor, Main Contractor or Employer is neither a company incorporated under the Companies Acts nor a company registered under the laws of another country, delete the references to Company number and registered office. In the case of a company incorporated outside England and Wales, particulars of its place of incorporation should be inserted immediately before its Company number.

And   (3)   _____

_____

_____ (Company No._____)[1]

of/whose registered office is at _____

_____

_____ ('the Employer',
which term shall include all permitted assignees under this Agreement).

Whereas

First   the Employer has entered into an agreement dated _____ with the Main
Contractor ('the Building Contract') for the carrying out of building works

_____

_____

_____ ('the Main Contract Works',
which term shall include any changes made to the building works in accordance with the Building
Contract);

Second   in relation to the Building Contract, the Sub-Contractor entered into an agreement ('the Sub-
Contract') dated _____ with the Main Contractor, to carry out and complete
certain works ('the Sub-Contract Works') forming part of the Main Contract Works;

Third   the Main Contractor is a Party to this Agreement for the purpose of giving the acknowledgements
set out in clauses 5 and 6·4;

Now it is hereby agreed as follows

In consideration of the payment of one pound (£1) by the Employer to each of the Contractor and the Sub-Contractor, receipt of which each acknowledges:

1   ·1   The Sub-Contractor warrants and undertakes to the Employer that he has complied and will continue to comply with the Sub-Contract. In the event of any breach of this warranty and subject to clauses 1·2, 1·3 and 1·4:

        ·1   the Sub-Contractor shall be liable for the reasonable costs of repair, renewal and/or reinstatement of any part or parts of the Sub-Contract Works to the extent that the Employer incurs such costs and/or the Employer is or becomes liable either directly or by way of financial contribution for such costs; and

        ·2   where the Warranty Particulars state that clause 1·1·2 applies, but subject to clause 1·2, the Sub-Contractor shall in addition to the costs referred to in clause 1·1·1 be liable for any other losses incurred by the Employer up to the limit, if any, stated in the Warranty Particulars;

    ·2   where in the Warranty Particulars no single liability option is selected for clause 1·1·2 or where the selected option has a limit but no amount is stated, the Sub-Contractor shall not be liable for any losses incurred by the Employer other than the costs referred to in clause 1·1·1;

    ·3   where the Warranty Particulars state that clause 1·3 applies and the Consultants are there identified, the Sub-Contractor's liability to the Employer under this Agreement shall be limited to the proportion of the Employer's losses which it would be just and equitable to require the Sub-Contractor to pay having regard to the extent of the Sub-Contractor's responsibility for the same, on the following assumptions, namely that:

        ·1   the Consultant(s) referred to in the Warranty Particulars has or have provided contractual undertakings to the Employer as regards the performance of his or their services in connection with the Main Contract Works in accordance with the terms of his or their respective consultancy agreements and that there are no limitations on liability as between the Consultant and the Employer in the consultancy agreement(s);

        ·2   the Main Contractor has provided contractual undertakings to the Employer that he has complied and will continue to comply with his obligations under the Building Contract but, for the purpose of this clause 1·3, excluding any liability for work sub-contracted to the Sub-Contractor;

        ·3   the Consultant(s) and the Main Contractor have paid to the Employer such proportion of the Employer's losses which it would be just and equitable for them to pay having regard to the extent of their responsibility for the Employer's losses;

    ·4   the Sub-Contractor shall be entitled in any action or proceedings by the Employer to rely on any term in the Sub-Contract and to raise the equivalent rights in defence of liability as he would have against the Main Contractor under the Sub-Contract;

    ·5   the obligations of the Sub-Contractor under or pursuant to this clause 1 shall not be released or diminished by the appointment of any person by the Employer to carry out any independent enquiry into any relevant matter.

2   The Sub-Contractor further warrants to the Employer that:

    ·1   he has exercised and will exercise reasonable skill, care and diligence in:

        ·1   the design of the Sub-Contract Works to the extent that such works have been or will be designed by the Sub-Contractor; and

        ·2   the selection of materials and goods for the Sub-Contract Works to the extent that such materials and goods have been or will be selected by the Sub-Contractor;

    ·2   he will satisfy any performance specification or requirement contained in or referred to in the Sub-Contract;

·3　he has not used nor will he use any materials or goods which at the time of use do not conform with British and European Standards or Codes of Practice; and that unless required by the Sub-Contract or unless otherwise authorised in writing by the Main Contractor, he has not used and will not use materials in the Sub-Contract Works other than in accordance with the guidelines contained in the edition of 'Good Practice in Selection of Construction Materials' (Ove Arup & Partners) current at the date of the Building Contract.

3　The Employer has no authority to issue any direction or instruction to the Sub-Contractor in relation to the Sub-Contract unless and until the Employer has given notice under clause 5 or 6·4.

4　The Employer has no liability to the Sub-Contractor in respect of amounts due under the Sub-Contract unless and until the Employer has given notice under clause 5 or 6·4.

5　The Sub-Contractor agrees that, in the event of the termination of the Main Contractor's employment under the Building Contract, the Sub-Contractor shall, if so required by written notice given by the Employer and subject to clause 7, accept the instructions of the Employer or his appointee to the exclusion of the Main Contractor in respect of the Sub-Contract Works upon the terms and conditions of the Sub-Contract. The Main Contractor acknowledges that the Sub-Contractor shall be entitled to rely on a notice given to the Sub-Contractor by the Employer under this clause 5 as conclusive evidence for the purposes of this Agreement of the termination of the Main Contractor's employment under the Building Contract; and further acknowledges that such acceptance of the instructions of the Employer to the exclusion of the Main Contractor shall not constitute any breach of the Sub-Contractor's obligations to the Main Contractor under the Sub-Contract.

6　·1　The Sub-Contractor shall not exercise any right of termination of his employment under the Sub-Contract without having first:

·1　copied to the Employer any notices required by the Sub-Contract to be sent to the Main Contractor prior to the Sub-Contractor being entitled to give notice under the Sub-Contract that his employment under the Sub-Contract is terminated; and

·2　given to the Employer written notice that the Sub-Contractor has the right under the Sub-Contract forthwith to notify the Main Contractor that his employment under the Sub-Contract is terminated.

·2　The Sub-Contractor shall not treat the Sub-Contract as having been repudiated by the Main Contractor without having first given to the Employer written notice that he intends so to notify the Main Contractor.

·3　The Sub-Contractor shall not:

·1　issue a notice to the Main Contractor to which clause 6·1·2 refers; or

·2　notify the Main Contractor that he is treating the Sub-Contract as having been repudiated by the Main Contractor as referred to in clause 6·2

before the lapse of 14 days from receipt by the Employer of the notice by the Sub-Contractor which the Sub-Contractor is required to give under clause 6·1·2 or 6·2.

·4　The Employer may, not later than the expiry of the period referred to in clause 6·3, require the Sub-Contractor by written notice and subject to clause 7 to accept the instructions of the Employer or his appointee to the exclusion of the Main Contractor in respect of the Sub-Contract Works upon the terms and conditions of the Sub-Contract. The Main Contractor acknowledges that the Sub-Contractor shall be entitled to rely on a notice given to the Sub-Contractor by the Employer under this clause 6·4 and that acceptance by the Sub-Contractor of the instruction of the Employer to the exclusion of the Main Contractor shall not constitute any breach of the Sub-Contractor's obligations to the Main Contractor under the Sub-Contract. Provided that nothing in this clause 6·4 shall relieve the Sub-Contractor of any liability he may have to the Main Contractor for any breach by the Sub-Contractor of the Sub-Contract.

7　It shall be a condition of any notice given by the Employer under clause 5 or 6·4 that the Employer accepts liability for payment of the sums due and payable to the Sub-Contractor under the Sub-Contract and for performance of the Main Contractor's obligations including payment of any sums outstanding at the date of such notice. Upon the issue of any notice by the Employer under clause 5 or 6·4, the Sub-Contract shall continue in full force and effect as if no right of termination of the Sub-Contractor's employment under the Sub-Contract, nor any right of the Sub-Contractor to treat the Sub-Contract as having been repudiated by the Main Contractor, had arisen and the Sub-Contractor shall be liable to the Employer under the Sub-Contract in lieu of his liability to the Main Contractor.

8   Where the Warranty Particulars state that clause 8 applies, the copyright in all drawings, reports, models, specifications, plans, schedules, bills of quantities, calculations and other similar documents prepared by or on behalf of the Sub-Contractor in connection with the Sub-Contract Works (together referred to as 'the Documents') shall remain vested in the Sub-Contractor but, subject to the Sub-Contractor having received all sums due and payable under the Sub-Contract, the Employer shall have an irrevocable, royalty-free, non-exclusive licence to copy and use the Documents and to reproduce the designs and content of them for any purpose relating to the Main Contract Works including, without limitation, the construction, completion, maintenance, letting, sale, promotion, advertisement, reinstatement, refurbishment and repair of the Main Contract Works. Such licence shall enable the Employer to copy and use the Documents for the extension of the Main Contract Works but shall not include a licence to reproduce the designs contained in them for any extension of the Main Contract Works. The Sub-Contractor shall not be liable for any such use by the Employer of any of the Documents for any purpose other than that for which they were prepared.

9   Where the Warranty Particulars state that clause 9 applies, the Sub-Contractor warrants that he has and shall maintain a Professional Indemnity insurance or Product Liability insurance policy (whichever is thereby stated to apply) with limits of indemnity of the types and in amounts not less than those there stated and for a period of the length there stated from the date of practical completion of the Main Contract Works (or, where the Building Contract provides for completion by Sections, practical completion of the relevant Section of the Main Contract Works), provided always that such insurance is available at commercially reasonable rates. The Sub-Contractor shall immediately give written notice to the Employer if such insurance ceases to be available at commercially reasonable rates in order that the Sub-Contractor and the Employer can discuss the means of best protecting their respective positions in respect of the Sub-Contract Works in the absence of such insurance. As and when reasonably requested to do so by the Employer or his appointee under clause 5 or 6·4, the Sub-Contractor shall produce for inspection documentary evidence that his insurance is being maintained.

10   This Agreement may be assigned without the Sub-Contractor's consent by the Employer, by way of absolute legal assignment, to another person (P1) and by P1, by way of absolute legal assignment, to another person (P2). In such cases the assignment shall only be effective upon written notice of it being given to the Sub-Contractor. No further or other assignment of this Agreement shall be permitted and in particular P2 shall not be entitled to assign this Agreement.

11   Any notice to be given by the Sub-Contractor to the Employer or by the Employer to the Sub-Contractor shall be duly given if delivered by hand or sent by Recorded Signed for or Special Delivery post to the recipient at such address as he may from time to time notify to the sender or (if no such address is then current) his last known principal business address or (where a body corporate) its registered or principal office. Where sent by post in that manner, it shall, subject to proof to the contrary, be deemed to have been received 48 hours after the date of posting.

12   No action or proceedings for any breach of this Agreement shall be commenced against the Sub-Contractor after the expiry of the relevant period from the date of practical completion of the Main Contract Works. Where the Main Contract provides for completion by Sections, no action or proceedings shall be commenced against the Sub-Contractor in respect of any Section after the expiry of the relevant period from the date of practical completion of such Section. For the purposes of this clause, the relevant period shall be:

·1   where this Agreement is executed under hand, 6 years; and

·2   where this Agreement is executed as a deed, 12 years.

13   This Agreement shall not negate or diminish any duty or liability otherwise owed by the Sub-Contractor to the Employer.

14   Notwithstanding any other provision of this Agreement nothing in this Agreement confers or is intended to confer any right to enforce any of its terms on any person who is not a party to it.

15   This Agreement shall be governed by and construed in accordance with the law of England and the English courts shall have jurisdiction over any dispute or difference.

*Note: An asterisk * indicates text that is to be deleted as appropriate.*

Clause	Subject	
1·1·2	Sub-Contractor's liability for other losses incurred by Employer	Clause 1·1·2 * applies/does not apply[2]
	Maximum liability options [3]	* Liability is limited to £ _____ in respect of each breach/ * Liability is limited to £ _____ under this Agreement/ * Liability is unlimited
1·3	Net Contribution	Clause 1·3 * applies/does not apply
1·3·1	Net Contribution: Consultants	For the purposes of clause 1·3·1 'the Consultants' are[4]: _____ _____ _____ _____
8	Copyright	Clause 8 * applies/does not apply
9	Professional Indemnity and Product Liability insurances	Clause 9 * applies/does not apply[5]
	Type of insurance	* Professional Indemnity insurance/ * Product Liability insurance

---

[2] Where clause 1·1·2 is required to apply, it is necessary, in addition to the appropriate deletion here, to select one of the liability options and where required to insert an amount – see clause 1·2 for effect if this is not done.

[3] Identify whichever option is to apply and where applicable insert an amount: delete the options not required.

[4] If clause 1·3 applies insert the discipline of the Consultant warrantors. If no Consultants are identified, the whole of clause 1·3 shall be deemed deleted.

[5] Delete "applies" if the Sub-Contractor is not required to produce any design.

Level of cover

Amount of indemnity required
* relates to claims or series of claims arising out
  of one event/
* ~~is the aggregate amount for any one period
  of insurance~~

and is

£ __2,500,000__

Cover for pollution and contamination claims
(if required)

£ _____

Expiry of required period of insurance is

* ~~6 years/~~
* 12 years/
* _____ years
  (not exceeding 12 years)

Note on Execution

This Agreement should be executed by all Parties, i.e. the Sub-Contractor, the Main Contractor and the Employer, either under hand or as a deed.

Execution under hand

If this Agreement is to be executed under hand, use the form set out on the following page. Each Party or his authorised representative should sign where indicated in the presence of a witness who should then sign and set out his name and address.

Execution as a Deed

If this Agreement is to be executed as a deed, each Party should use the relevant form marked 'Execution as a Deed' in accordance with the notes provided.

Other forms of Attestation

In cases where the forms of attestation set out are not appropriate, e.g. in the case of certain housing associations and partnerships or if a Party wishes an attorney to execute this Agreement on his behalf, the appropriate form(s) may be inserted in the vacant space opposite and/or below.

Execution under hand

As witness

the hands of the Parties
or their duly authorised representatives

Signed by or on behalf of
the Sub-Contractor

_____

in the presence of:

_____
witness' signature

_____
witness' name

_____
witness' address

_____

Signed by or on behalf of
the Main Contractor

_____

in the presence of:

_____
witness' signature

_____
witness' name

_____
witness' address

_____

Signed by or on behalf of
the Employer

_____

in the presence of:

_____
witness' signature

_____
witness' name

_____
witness' address

_____

Notes on Execution as a Deed

1   For the purposes of execution as a deed, three forms are provided for execution, one for the Sub-Contractor, one for the Main Contractor and the other for the Employer. Each form provides four methods of execution, **(A)** to **(D)**, for use as appropriate. The full name of the Sub-Contractor, Main Contractor or Employer (whether an individual, a company or other body) should be inserted where indicated at the commencement of the relevant form. This applies irrespective of the method used.

2   For public and private companies incorporated and registered under the Companies Acts, the three principal methods of execution as a deed are:

   (A)   through signature by a Director and the Company Secretary or by two Directors;

   (B)   by affixing the company's common seal in the presence of a Director and the *Company* Secretary or of two Directors or other duly authorised officers; or

   (C)   signature by a single Director in the presence of a witness who attests the signature.

   Methods **(A)** and **(C)** are available to public and private companies whether or not they have a common seal. (Method **(C)** was introduced by section 44(2)(b) of the Companies Act 2006.) Methods **(A)** and **(C)** are not available under companies legislation to local authorities or to certain other bodies corporate, e.g. bodies incorporated by letters patent or private Act of Parliament that are not registered under companies legislation and such bodies may only use method **(B)**.

3   Where method **(A)** is being used, delete the inappropriate words and insert in the spaces indicated the names of the two Directors, or of the Director and the Company Secretary, who are to sign.

4   If method **(B)** (affixing the common seal) is adopted in cases where either or both the authorised officers attesting its affixation are not themselves a Director or the *Company* Secretary, their respective office(s) should be substituted for the reference(s) to Director and/or to *Company* Secretary/Director. (In the case of execution by bodies that are not companies, the reference to "*Company*" under the second signature should be deleted where appropriate.)

5   Method **(C)** (execution by a single Director) has been introduced primarily, but not exclusively, for 'single officer' companies. The Director should sign where indicated in the presence of a witness who should then sign and set out his name and address.

6   Where the Sub-Contractor, Main Contractor or Employer is an individual, he should use method **(D)** and sign where indicated in the presence of a witness who should then sign and set out his name and address.

Executed as a Deed by the Sub-Contractor

namely [1] _____

(A)   acting by a Director and the Company Secretary/two Directors **of the company** [2, 3]

_____   and   _____
(Print name of signatory)   *(Print name of signatory)*

_____   _____
Signature   Director   *Signature*   Company Secretary/Director

(B)   by affixing hereto the common seal **of the company/other body corporate** [2, 4]

in the presence of

_____
Signature   Director

_____
Signature   Company Secretary/Director

[Common seal of company]

(C)   by attested signature of a single Director **of the company** [2, 5]

_____
Signature   Director

in the presence of

Witness' signature _____ *(Print name)* _____

Witness' address _____

(D)   by attested signature **of the individual** [6]

_____
Signature

in the presence of

Witness' signature _____ *(Print name)* _____

Witness' address _____

Note: The numbers on this page refer to the numbered paragraphs in the Notes on Execution as a Deed.

Executed as a Deed by the Main Contractor

namely ¹ _____

(A) acting by a Director and the Company Secretary/two Directors **of the company** ²'³

_____   and   _____
(Print name of signatory)   *(Print name of signatory)*

_____   _____
Signature   Director   *Signature*   Company Secretary/Director

(B) by affixing hereto the common seal **of the company/other body corporate** ²'⁴

in the presence of

_____
Signature   Director

_____
Signature   Company Secretary/Director

[Common seal of company]

(C) by attested signature of a single Director **of the company** ²'⁵

_____
Signature   Director

in the presence of

Witness' signature _____ *(Print name)* _____

Witness' address _____

(D) by attested signature **of the individual** ⁶

_____
Signature

in the presence of

Witness' signature _____ *(Print name)* _____

Witness' address _____

Note: The numbers on this page refer to the numbered paragraphs in the Notes on Execution as a Deed.

Executed as a Deed by the Employer

namely [1] _____

(A)   acting by a Director and the Company Secretary/two Directors **of the company** [2, 3]

_____   and   _____
(Print name of signatory)   *(Print name of signatory)*

_____   _____
Signature   Director   *Signature*   Company Secretary/Director

(B)   by affixing hereto the common seal **of the company/other body corporate** [2, 4]

in the presence of

_____
Signature   Director

_____
Signature   Company Secretary/Director   *[Common seal of company]*

(C)   by attested signature of a single Director **of the company** [2, 5]

_____
         Signature   Director

in the presence of

Witness' signature   _____   *(Print name)* _____

Witness' address   _____

(D)   by attested signature **of the individual** [6]

_____
         Signature

in the presence of

Witness' signature   _____   *(Print name)* _____

Witness' address   _____

Note: The numbers on this page refer to the numbered paragraphs in the Notes on Execution as a Deed.

Guidance Notes

General

The JCT Warranty SCWa/E 2011 is for use with contracts let under SBC, IC, ICD, DB and PCC where the Employer has an agreement with a person ('Main Contractor') who will carry out building works ('Main Contract Works') required by the Employer.

Warranty SCWa/E is collateral to the Sub-Contract and, generally, should not be entered into before the date of the Sub-Contract. Under the enabling clause in the respective contract, the Sub-Contractor may be required to enter into the warranty.

The Warranty Particulars require completion. Where the Warranty may be required to be entered into after the date of the Sub-Contract, it is essential that, pre-contract, the Sub-Contractor is informed:

- of the way in which the clauses requiring completion within the Warranty will be completed; if subsequently, the Warranty is to be completed on different terms then the agreement of the Sub-Contractor to those different terms would be required; and

- if the Employer seeks to make any amendments to the terms of the Warranty SCWa/E which he will require the Sub-Contractor (through the Main Contractor) to give, then the amendments must be set out as part of the Sub-Contract tender documentation. **Amendments to the clauses of the Warranty SCWa/E should however be avoided.**

Commentary

Parties and Recitals

The Parties and the first two Recitals require completion and should conform with the notice to the Sub-Contractor that requires him to execute this Warranty. Care should be taken in that notice to give the correct particulars of the Employer.

As stated in the Third Recital, the Main Contractor is a Party to this Agreement for the purposes of the acknowledgements given in clauses 5 and 6·4. This is to allow the Sub-Contractor to comply with the obligations imposed upon him under those clauses, without being liable to the Main Contractor for breach of contract.

Clause 1

This confirms that the Sub-Contractor owes the same obligation to the Employer as he owes to the Main Contractor under the Sub-Contract, but subject to clauses 1·2, 1·3 and 1·4.

Clauses 1·2, 1·3 and 1·4, where applicable, qualify and limit the Sub-Contractor's liability in the event of a breach by the Sub-Contractor of the Sub-Contract.

This Warranty provides under clause 1·1 that the Sub-Contractor is liable for the reasonable costs of repair, renewal and/or reinstatement of the Sub-Contract Works to the extent that the Employer incurs such costs or becomes liable for such costs. Additionally, the Sub-Contractor may be made liable for further losses under clause 1·1·2 if in the Warranty Particulars it is stated that clause 1·1·2 applies. Clause 1·1·2 provides in the Warranty Particulars for optional provisions whereby the losses are capped either in respect of each breach or in respect of an aggregate; the amount of any financial cap is to be inserted. The unlimited liability option should be selected if a financial cap is not to apply. Whenever practicable the Employer, bearing in mind his obligation to mitigate damages he has suffered, should inform the Sub-Contractor of the defects prior to having them repaired and consider any offer by the Sub-Contractor to carry out the repair.

Clause 1·2 is intended to make it clear that, where an option is not selected or where one is selected but 'no amount' is inserted in the entries for clause 1·1·2 of the Warranty Particulars, the Sub-Contractor is only liable for the losses referred to in clause 1·1·1.

Where clause 1·3 applies, it is also intended to limit the Sub-Contractor's potential liability. The

Warranty given by the Sub-Contractor is based on the assumptions set out in clauses 1·3·1 to 1·3·3 and the limitation applies whether or not the Consultants employed by the Employer and/or the Main Contractor have actually given contractual undertakings to the Employer. If no Consultants are identified against clause 1·3·1 in the Warranty Particulars, even though the clause is stated to apply, the whole of clause 1·3 shall be deemed deleted (see footnote [4]).

By clause 1·4, and subject to clause 1·3, the Employer is intended to be in a similar position to the Main Contractor in terms of enforcing rights under the Sub-Contract in that the Sub-Contractor may raise against the Employer the same defences of liability as he could against the Main Contractor.

Clause 1·5 records that the appointment by the Employer of any consultant (e.g. to survey the buildings comprising the Main Contract Works) shall not affect any liability which the Sub-Contractor may have under clause 1.

Clause 2

The Sub-Contractor warrants that he will satisfy any performance specification or requirement referred to in the Sub-Contract and where he is involved in designing the Sub-Contract Works that he will use reasonable skill, care and diligence.

The Sub-Contractor also warrants that he has not used and will not use materials in the Sub-Contract Works other than in accordance with the guidelines contained in the publication 'Good Practice in Selection of Construction Materials'. Clause 2 excuses the use by the Sub-Contractor of other materials if the use has been required or authorised in writing by the Main Contractor, though it should be noted that the Sub-Contractor will in appropriate circumstances have a duty to warn against such use.

Clause 3

This is included to make it clear that the Employer has no power or authority to instruct the Sub-Contractor in his duties to the Main Contractor under the Sub-Contract. This is however subject to the Employer's rights under clause 5, following termination of the Main Contractor's employment under the Building Contract, or under clause 6·4.

Clause 4

As indicated by this clause, the Employer has no liability for any amounts due under the Sub-Contract until he has given a notice under clause 5 or 6·4.

Clauses 5, 6 and 7

These clauses entitle the Employer to 'step in' and take over as employer of the Sub-Contractor and oblige the Sub-Contractor to accept the instructions of the Employer, if the Employer so decides, in circumstances where the Main Contractor's employment is terminated or the Sub-Contractor intends to terminate his own employment under the Sub-Contract.

To give the Employer a reasonable time to decide whether to 'step in' under clause 6·4, clause 6·1 requires the Sub-Contractor to copy to the Employer any warning notice which has to be given under the Sub-Contract before the Sub-Contractor can give notice to the Main Contractor that the Sub-Contractor's employment is terminated or, alternatively, to notify the Employer if the Sub-Contractor considers that the Main Contractor has repudiated the Sub-Contract.

If the Sub-Contractor:

- is subsequently in a position to give to the Main Contractor actual notice of termination of the Sub-Contractor's employment under the Sub-Contract; or

- intends to notify the Main Contractor that he is treating the Sub-Contract as having been repudiated by the Main Contractor,

the Sub-Contractor, by clause 6·3, may give such notice to the Main Contractor but not without having first given the Employer at least 14 days notice that the Sub-Contractor's right to termination has actually arisen or, in the case of repudiation, that he intends so to notify the Main Contractor.

The Employer may within that period act under clause 6·4 and give notice that he will take over the rights and obligations of the Main Contractor but on the terms of clause 7 in regard to the Employer accepting all the liabilities of the Main Contractor at the date of the takeover and agreeing to perform all the Main Contractor's obligations under the Sub-Contract.

Clause 8

This clause will normally only be applicable where the Sub-Contractor carries out a design function in relation to the Sub-Contract Works; the Warranty Particulars are required to state whether or not clause 8 applies. Reasonable use by the Employer of drawings and associated documents is necessary in most cases. By this clause the Employer is given the rights that might reasonably be expected but it does not allow the reproduction of the designs for any purpose outside the scope of the Main Contract Works; such reproduction would require a further agreement with the Sub-Contractor.

Clause 9

This clause will only be applicable where the Sub-Contractor carries out a design function. The Warranty Particulars are required to state whether or not clause 9 applies and, where it does apply, the type of insurance, the level of cover required, including any amount within that cover that is required for pollution and contamination claims. The Warranty Particulars should also state the period of insurance required. Where clause 9 applies, it should be noted that:

- the obligation to maintain Professional Indemnity insurance or Product Liability insurance is subject to the proviso that such insurance continues to be available at commercially reasonable rates; if after the insurance has been taken out the rates upon any renewal cease to be commercially reasonable the Sub-Contractor must inform the Employer;

- Product Liability insurance cover is not a substitute or alternative to Professional Indemnity insurance but may be of some limited benefit in certain circumstances;

- not all Sub-Contractors will have, or can obtain, Professional Indemnity insurance or Product Liability insurance and Employers must recognise this when seeking to operate the terms of clause 9.

Clause 10

This clause indicates the right of assignment by the Employer.

Clause 11

This clause sets out the required methods of giving notice under this Agreement.

Clause 12

This clause makes clear that, unless proceedings have previously been commenced, any liability that the Sub-Contractor has under this Warranty ceases on the expiry of the relevant period from the date of practical completion of the Main Contract Works (or, where completed in Sections, practical completion of the relevant Section).

The relevant period is 6 or 12 years depending on whether this Agreement is to be executed under hand or executed as a deed – see Attestation below.

Clause 13

This clause is to make clear that this Agreement does not affect any other obligations that the Sub-Contractor might have to the Employer.

Clause 14

The JCT has agreed that this Warranty should contract out of the Contracts (Rights of Third Parties) Act 1999.

Clause 15

It will be noted that this Agreement is to be governed by English law and that the English courts shall have jurisdiction over any dispute or difference. If the Sub-Contract provides that it is to be governed by the law of any other jurisdiction, this Warranty should generally be conformed with it.

Disputes under this Agreement are not intended to be referable to arbitration unless the Sub-Contractor and the Employer otherwise agree, in which case a provision relating to the reference to arbitration and the conduct of any arbitration may be inserted. However, if an Employer 'steps in' to replace the Main Contractor under the Sub-Contract (see clauses 5 and 6·4), the dispute resolution provisions of the Sub-Contract would continue to apply to any dispute arising out of or in connection with that contract.

Attestation

The prescribed mode of execution is in general intended to follow the mode adopted for the Building Contract, i.e. where the latter is executed as a deed, this Agreement should also be executed as a deed and, where executed under hand, this Agreement may also be executed under hand.

2011 changes

The following provisions in 2011 Edition contain minor textual changes.

2011 numbering

Warranty Agreement (clauses)
6·4
9

Warranty Particulars (entries)
9